The Saw That Talked

First published in 2013 by Grass Roots Press

Grass Roots Press gratefully acknowledges the financial support for its publishing programs provided by the following agencies: the Government of Canada through the Canada Book Fund and the Government of Alberta through the Alberta Foundation for the Arts.

Library and Archives Canada Cataloguing in Publication

Reiff, Tana
    The saw that talked / Tana Reiff. — Rev. ed.

(Pathfinders)
ISBN 978–1–927499–70–2

        1. Readers (Adult). 2. Readers for new literates.
I. Title. II. Series: Pathfinders (Edmonton, Alta.)

PE1126.A4R445 2013   428.6'2   C2012–906779–2

Cover image: © robcocquyt/istockphoto

The Saw That Talked
Tana Reiff

PATHFINDERS

Grass Roots Press

Chapter 1

When Lindy
was a young girl,
the tree
in front of her house
was hit
during a storm.
It was a big tree.
Lindy would never forget
how the earth shook
when the tree
hit the ground.
After the storm
she and her big brother
went outside
to take a look.

"Look at all this wood!"
her brother said.
"Just think
of all the things
we can make!"

The next week
their father
took a chainsaw
to the fallen tree.
Then Lindy and her brother
had their turn.
They knocked off the bark.
They sawed logs
into smaller pieces.
They carried
all of it
into their dad's workroom.
There, they began
to make things
out of wood.

They sawed.
They shaped.
They nailed.
They sanded.
They worked together
for many weeks.

One piece of wood
became a little table

for Lindy.
Others became
little chairs
for Lindy and her friends.
The last thing
Lindy and her brother made
was a house
for their dog.

From that time on,
Lindy loved wood.
She loved
the look of wood.
She loved
the feel of wood.
She loved
the smell of sawdust.
She loved
to turn a piece of wood
into something
that someone could use.

When Lindy
got to high school,
she took wood shop.

She was
the only girl
in the class.
It didn't matter.
When Lindy
was in the wood shop,
she was happy.
She liked it so much
that she went on
to carpentry school.

And then,
when Lindy
got out of school,
she looked
for a job
working with wood.
She found one
in a small furniture factory.

Around the same time,
she married Nick.
Lindy felt
very lucky.

Chapter 2

It was Lindy's first day
working in the wood shop.
She met the owner,
Chet Michaels.
He showed her
to the saw table
where she would work.

Lindy's job
was to cut boards
into set shapes.
Each board would become
the side or front or back
of a chair or sofa.

Lindy did her job
standing at the saw table.
The round blade
of the saw
was spinning all the time.
With one hand,

Lindy held the board
against the back
of the table.
With the other hand,
she pulled the saw handle
toward her.
The spinning blade
cut each board
along the marks.

Lindy had worked
with table saws before.
But something was missing
from this one.
There was no guard
on the blade.
At carpentry school,
every saw blade
had a guard.
She didn't have to worry
if her hand slipped.
The guard made sure
she would not
hit the blade.

But her saw blade
at the furniture factory
had no guard.

She felt
she should say something
to Chet Michaels.
She went over and over it
in her head.
But she was afraid
to speak up.
She had just started
this new job.

And Lindy
was the only woman
on this floor.
She didn't want
to look weak.
She didn't want
to stand out.
After all,
no one had guards
on their saw blades.

So she couldn't talk to Chet.
And there was no way
she was going to talk
to these guys
about a blade guard.
They would only laugh,
the way they always did.

They would start on her
the minute
she got to work.

"Hey there, sweet thing!"
a guy named Burt Flowers
called to her.

"Here comes
the pretty woman!"
said another.

Lindy liked her work.
But she hated
hearing those guys.
She couldn't make friends
with any of these people.

No, she could not
talk to them
about the blade guards.

She was glad
to have Nick,
because at work
she felt all alone.

And what if
she lost her job
just for talking
about blade guards?
This was not
a union shop.
There was no one
to stand up for Lindy
but Lindy herself.
She felt
she was in no place
to stand up for herself here.

She made up her mind.
Speaking up
just wasn't worth it.

So Lindy
kept her mouth shut.
She could work
with a blade
that had no guard.
She would just have to be
very careful.

Chapter 3

Lindy's job
in the wood shop
was going all right.
She was turning out
chair and sofa frames
one after another.

The one thing
she still didn't like
was the way
the guys acted.
Not only did they
check her out
every day,
they gave her
a bad time
in other ways too.
They always found
a new way
to bug her.

"Hey Lindy!
Don't break a nail
on that saw table!"
one guy kept saying.

Lindy always
looked him in the eye.
She always kept
her mouth shut tight
to keep in the words
she really wanted to say.

They also played tricks.
One day,
the guys locked her
out of the lunchroom.
Another time,
they took the key
to the ladies' room.
All she could do
was use the men's room.

Then one day
one of the guys
went a step too far.

Lindy was working
at the saw table.
She was cutting boards
just like always.
She was keeping
a close eye
on her blade.
It was loud
on the shop floor.
But she heard
one of the guys call out,
"Lindy! Hey, Lindy!
Watch out!
There's a board
flying at you!"

Lindy looked up
as she reached
for the handle
on the saw.
She saw nothing
to watch out for.

All of a sudden,
all she could hear

was her own scream.
Instead of the handle,
she had reached
right into the blade.
The end
of her little finger
hit the blade.
She saw the blood
flowing out of her finger.

"What do I do now?"
she cried.
She looked around,
hoping someone would help her.

Chapter 4

Lindy leaned back
against the wall.
The pain in one finger
filled her whole body.
But she didn't want the guys
to know how bad she felt.

One of the older men
ran over to Lindy.
"What happened?"
Brady asked
in a kind voice.
Then he saw for himself.
"Let me see
your finger."

By this time
Lindy was crying.
She didn't want anyone
to see her crying.
But she couldn't help it.

The pain was so bad,
she felt sick and dizzy.

Brady took a look
at the finger.
"You lost
the end of it,"
he told Lindy.
He pulled a rag
from his pocket.
He wrapped her finger
to stop the blood.

"Thanks, Brady,"
said Lindy.
"I guess I'd better
go and see
the company nurse."

"I wouldn't do that,"
said Brady.
"Around here,
we don't get hurt
on the job."

"What do you mean?"
Lindy wanted to know.
"I just lost
part of my finger.
I'd say
I just got hurt
on the job."

"You want to keep
your job?"
Brady asked.
"Then don't go
to the company nurse.
Go to your family doctor.
If you go
to the company nurse,
you won't have a job
to come back to."

"You're kidding!"
said Lindy.

"I wish,"
said Brady.
"That's how it is here.

Now my word to you is,
put on a smile
and get back
to your saw table."

To Lindy,
one cut finger
felt as if her hand
had been cut off.
She tried not to cry.
She didn't want
her pain to show.
But her finger
hurt like crazy.
She didn't see
how she could go
back to that saw table.

But back she went.
She tried not to think
about her finger.
She put her mind
on the next board.
And the next.
And the next.

And with every board
she sawed,
she kept her eye
on that blade.
She had let her mind
leave her work once.
For that, she had paid.
She couldn't let it
happen again.

At long last,
her shift was over.
Lindy felt very weak.
The pain in her finger
was all she could think about.
She dragged herself
to her car.
She grabbed
the door handle.
She fell
into the front seat.
Her head
dropped to the wheel
and she let herself
cry like a baby.

Chapter 5

"What happened to you?"
Nick cried
when he saw Lindy.

She told her husband
what had happened.
"And you drove home?"
he wondered.
"You're in bad shape.
How in the world
did you drive a car?"

"It's only my finger,"
said Lindy.

"Get in the car,"
said Nick.
"I'm taking you
to Emergency."

On the way,
Lindy and Nick talked.
"Why didn't you go
to the company nurse?"
Nick wanted to know.
"Why didn't you
tell your boss?"

"I didn't want
to get fired,"
said Lindy.
"Brady said
to shut up
or I'd be fired."

"Well, then, call
the Health and Safety inspectors,"
said Nick.
"They won't let
your company
get away with
not having blade guards.
Hey, I'll call *for* you!"

"No way!"
said Lindy.
"You and I both know
there should be guards
on those blades.
But anyone
who rocks the boat
is in for rough sailing.
Besides, Nick,
I'm the only woman
on my floor.
I have to be tough.
I'm not going to be
the one who talks.
I just have to be
more careful."

"I want to know
why there aren't guards
on those blades,"
said Nick.

"They tell me
blade guards
slow things down,"

said Lindy.
"You must set the blade
for the size
of the board.
It's hard to see
how to set it
with the guard on.
You can pull a blade out more
when there's no guard.
That saves time.
Time is money, man.
And money
is what the company
cares about."

"How do they
get away with it?"
Nick wanted to know.

"They get away with it
until someone calls
the inspectors,"
said Lindy.
"And no one calls.

So the inspectors
don't see it."

"Why don't the inspectors
come and take a look
now and then?"
Nick wondered.

"There aren't
enough inspectors
to check up
all the time,"
she said.
She reached
deep into her bag.

"What are you doing?"
Nick asked.

"I have the number
for Health and Safety,"
Lindy told him.
"I keep it
in my bag.

In a pocket.
Deep down here
somewhere."

She dug into her bag.
"Here it is,"
she said
as she pulled out
the little paper.

"Well, I hope
you'll use it,"
said Nick.
"Because if you don't,
I will."

Nick drove
to Emergency.
A doctor looked
at Lindy's little finger.
"You had a close call,"
he told her.
He began to stitch.
"You were lucky

you didn't cut off
the whole finger,"
he went on.
Or your whole hand,
for that matter!
You really should not work
for a little while."

"Maybe not,"
said Lindy.
"But I can't miss work
for one bad finger.
I'll be there tomorrow
pain or no pain."

Chapter 6

Lindy stood
at her saw table
the very next morning.
The little finger
on her right hand
was wrapped in white.

"How's your finger?"
Brady asked her.

"No big deal,"
she told him.
"I didn't need
the end of that finger!"
They both laughed.

And so, work went on,
the same as always.

On Friday afternoon
Lindy was finishing up

for the week.
There were only
ten more boards
to saw.
She counted down:
9, 8, 7.
And then six.

That Friday,
six was not
Lindy's lucky number.

She held that board
against the back
of the saw table.
The saw
cut into the board.
All of a sudden,
the blade
hit a tiny knot
in the wood.
The board jumped.
Lindy wasn't ready.
It all happened
so fast.

Her thumb
hit the saw blade.
Lindy cried out in pain.
She backed off fast.
She could see
that her thumb
was cut real bad.
Blood was everywhere.

This time,
Brady heard her cry out.
He ran over to Lindy
and wrapped a rag
around her thumb.

Lindy held her mouth tight
as if to hold in the pain.

"I'll be okay,"
Lindy told Brady.
"It's not that bad."

She finished sawing
the last five boards.

Then she drove herself
to Emergency.

But Lindy had to stay home
the next day.
The pain was still too bad.
She lost a day of work,
a day's pay.

And then, a week later,
Lindy was in the middle
of sawing a board.
Little bits of wood
began to fly all over.
Lindy ducked.
This happened
all the time.
But this time,
some of the bits
hit Lindy in the face.
She felt a line
of hot blood
drip down her cheek.

She knew why
the wood
flew around like that.
It was because
there was no guard
on the saw blade.

Just then,
Chet Michaels
came walking by.
"What's up, kid?"
he asked her.

Lindy hated
when Chet called her "kid."
He never called
the guys "kid."
Only her.
Only the woman.

"Nothing's up,"
she answered.
"I can handle
a little blood."

"Yes, I guess you can,"
said Chet.
"You should be
used to it by now.
Maybe you should be
a little more careful
around that saw.
You, of all people,
should keep your eyes
on your blade."

Lindy was afraid
she might blow up.
She had just been hit
in the face
with flying wood.
It was because
there were no guards
on the blade.
And Chet picked now
to tell her
to be more careful.

"Yeah. I'll be more careful,"
Lindy told Chet.
But Chet Michaels
had not heard the last
of what Lindy had to say.

Chapter 7

Enough was enough.
Lindy was ready
to call the inspectors.
Health and Safety
needed to know
what was going on
at this furniture factory.

The company
had a rule:
No phones
on the shop floor.
No calls, no texts,
no games, nothing.

So Lindy waited
till break time.
Then she marched
out the door.
She kept on walking,

to be as far away
as she could be.

She dug deep
into her bag.
She pulled out
the phone number.

She hoped
to talk to someone
right away.
But she was put
on hold.
She waited.
And waited.
She looked
at the time.
Her break
was almost over.
She gave up
and went back inside.

Over lunch
she called again.
She ate her lunch outside

while she waited
on hold.
She heard
the same music
playing over and over.

And then, at last,
she heard a voice.
"How can we help you?"
the man said.

"I need to report
the company I work for,"
she began.
She told the man
all about her saw
with no blade guard.
She told him
about how she got hurt,
three times.

"Are you following
all the safety rules?"
the man asked.

"Of course, I am!"
said Lindy.
"But the company
is not!
That is who
won't keep guards
on the blades,
not me!"

"Are you sure
you're not just angry
about something else?"
the man asked.

"I'm angry
about a lot of things,"
said Lindy.
"But there are still
no guards on the blades!"

"We're pretty busy,"
said the man.
"But we *will* send
someone to take a look.

It won't be
today or tomorrow."

"Thank you,"
was all Lindy said.
With that,
she ended the call
and went back inside.

She had done it.
She had called
the inspectors.
Now she had to wait
for two things.
She had to wait
for an inspector
to show up.
And she had to wait
to see if this phone call
would cost her
a job she loved.

Chapter 8

A week went by.
No inspector
came to the shop.
Two weeks passed.
Still no one.

No one was talking much
these days.
Lindy did not tell anyone
about her phone call.
The guys had stopped
giving Lindy a hard time.
They knew
they had gone too far.
Seeing Lindy get hurt
was not funny.

Then one day,
Lindy heard a man cry out
over the sound
of the saws.

"It got me!
Oh, God, it got me!"

It was Brady.
Lindy ran over
to see what was wrong.
She saw Brady's hand,
covered with blood.

"What happened?"
she called to Brady.

Brady didn't answer.
His face went blank.
He fell to the floor.
A circle of blood
formed a pool
around him.
Brady was out cold.

One of the other guys
came over
to Brady's saw table.
"Look at that!"

he screamed,
pointing to Brady
on the floor.

Lindy got down on the floor
beside Brady.
She looked at his hand.
It was cut wide open
to the bone.
She knew at once
what had happened.
Brady's hand had slipped.
And his saw blade
had cut right into it.

"Is anyone here
going to say
this man
shouldn't see
the company nurse?"
shouted Lindy.
She looked around.
All the guys
had stopped working.

The whole place
was still and quiet now.
Everyone was looking
at Lindy.
No one answered her.

"Does anyone hear me?"
she asked.
"I don't think
Brady should be moved.
And we can't leave him here
like this.
He'll die.
He has lost
a lot of blood.
I'm going
for the nurse."

One of the guys
got down on the floor
to check Brady.
"He needs more
than the company nurse,"
he said.

Lindy ran to the door.
She heard
one of the guys say,
"There should be guards
on these blades."
Another guy said,
"Someone around here
should have called
the inspectors
a long time ago."

"Guess what?"
Lindy called out.
"I already did!
Now what do you think
of that?"

Chapter 9

Lindy and the nurse
came running back
to the shop floor.
The nurse said
that Brady must go
to a hospital
right away.

In minutes,
help came.
The paramedics
carried Brady out.
Lindy waved goodbye
and off they went,
lights flashing.

Lindy headed back
to the shop floor.
She turned
down the hall.
What she saw there

made her stop
in her tracks.

All the men
were standing around
with phones
in their hands.

"What's going on, guys?"
she asked.

"We're calling
the inspectors,"
said one.
"We're all reporting
the blades without guards."

"You're kidding!"
she laughed.
"All you guys are calling
at the same time?"

"No phones
on the shop floor,"
said Burt Flowers.

"That's the rule.
So here we are."

"No service!"
one guy shouted out.
"Too many calling
at the same time!"

But some of the calls
were getting through.

"You started it, girl!"
said Burt Flowers.

"All right!"
said Lindy.
Her smile
was as wide
as a big, round saw blade.

"If we all call,
maybe we'll get guards
on our blades,"
Burt said.

"Some of the guys
don't like the guards.
But wait till you get hurt!
And what's the worst
that can happen?
If one of us gets fired,
we all get fired!"

"We're in this together!"
said Lindy.

She heard a guy talking
on his phone.
"Someone here
got hurt real bad.
You need to come and look.
These saw blades
with no guards
could kill someone!"

The next day
an inspector
showed up at the shop.
It took him

less than a minute
to spot the problem.

"You have 30 days
to get a guard
on every blade,"
the inspector told Chet Michaels.
"I'll be back
to have a look.
If there are no guards,
no one can use the saws.
Got that?"

Chapter 10

Two weeks later
every saw
on that shop floor
had a blade guard.
It took a little time
to get used to the guards.
They did slow down the work
a little bit.
But everyone felt
much safer.

Brady's hand
was in bad shape.
He was still in hospital
when guards
were put on the saw blades.
Lindy went to visit him.

"We did it, Brady!"
said Lindy.

"Now there's one more thing
we have to do.
File you a claim
for Workers' Compensation."

"You really are crazy, girl,"
said Brady.
"You got things
all stirred up.
That's great.
No one even lost their job.
But now you want me
to stir things up more
by filing a claim?
Are you mad?"

"Dear Brady,
you can't use your hand,"
said Lindy.
"Do you want
to lose pay
for all your lost time?
Look at you.
You'll be out of work

for a long time.
You might never be able
to work a saw again!"

"That's life,"
said Brady.

"Listen, I'll help you file,"
said Lindy.
"I don't know
much about it.
But I'll find out.
We don't have a union.
We have to help each other."

"You're young, Lindy,"
said Brady.
"I've worked
for Chet Michaels
all my life.
I can't turn on him
after all these years."

"You're not turning on him,"
said Lindy.
"You'll need the money.
That's why the company
pays into Workers' Comp.
You could sue
for not having guards
on the blades!"

The next day
Lindy went
to the company office.
She asked
for a claim form
for Brady.
She asked for one
for herself too.
Maybe she could get paid
for her lost day of work.

"We'll fill out
the claim forms for you,"
she was told.

"No, thanks,"
Lindy said.
"I'll take them with me."

She and Brady
filled out the forms together.
They had to get doctors
to fill out some parts
and then sign the forms.
Lindy took the forms back
to the company office.
The company
needed to fill out
one part of the form.
Then the company needed
to send the claims
to the insurance company.

Lindy and Brady
waited to hear
about their claims.
But word did not come.
So Lindy called
the insurance company.

"We never got your claims,"
she was told.

"I knew it!"
Brady said.
"The company
never filed the claims!"

"Right,"
said Lindy.
"They would have
sent us copies
if they had filed them."

"We shouldn't have
tried to file,"
said Brady.

"No, no, no,"
said Lindy.
"We had to file.
We just need
to get the guys
behind us on this."

Chapter 11

When Brady was back home,
Lindy went to his house.
"You're coming with me
to the shop today,"
she told him.

"What's going on?"
Brady asked her.

"You'll see,"
Lindy said
as she helped Brady
to her car.

When they got
to the wood shop,
Lindy told everyone
about the lost claims.
They all stopped
what they were doing.

They marched down
to the company office.
Lindy walked
at the head of the parade.
Brady was second.

The woman at the desk
was Barbara Michaels.
She was Chet's wife.
She ran the office.

"What happened
to our Workers' Comp claims?"
Lindy asked Barbara Michaels.

"Nothing,"
said Barbara.
Sure enough,
two claim forms—
hers and Brady's—
were sitting on the desk.
"I was told
not to file these claims.
I'm sorry."

Lindy grabbed the claims.
"You haven't even filled out
the company's part
of the form!"
she said.
"We're not leaving
until these forms
are ready to send."

Barbara pressed
a button
on the desk phone.
"Chet, you'd better
get over here,"
she said.

All the workers
packed into the little office.
They watched
as Chet worked
on the form.
He asked Brady and Lindy
some questions
along the way.

They checked
to make sure
everything on the form
was correct and true.
Everyone watched
as Chet signed
both claim forms.
They watched
as Barbara put the forms
in a big envelope.
They watched
as she wrote the address
on the envelope.
They watched
as she put postage
on the envelope.
And they stayed
until the mail truck came.
They watched
as it drove away
with the envelope inside it.

The workers
walked back

to the wood shop.
This time,
Lindy and Brady
were at the tail end
of the parade.

"Do you think
we'll get Workers' Comp?"
Brady asked Lindy.

"We'll see,"
Lindy said.
She gave Brady
a big hug.

"Thanks, girl,"
said Brady
with wet eyes.
"Everything is better
because of you."

Lindy thought back
to when she was a child.
She thought about

when the big tree
came down
in the storm.
She thought about
how she and her brother
made things
out of the wood.
She told the story
to Brady.

"Just when you think
everything is coming down
around you,
you make something
good out of it,"
Brady smiled.

As they reached
the wood shop,
Lindy smelled the sawdust.
She couldn't wait
to get in there
and cut some more wood.

Made in the USA
Middletown, DE
14 March 2021